THE
PHOENIX

A WOMEN'S ROADMAP TO
IDENTIFY SELF

JULI MARIE M.ED

WRITERS REPUBLIC L.L.C.
515 Summit Ave. Unit R1
Union City, NJ 07087, USA

Website: *www.writersrepublic.com*
Hotline: *1-877-656-6838*
Email: *info@writersrepublic.com*

Ordering Information:
Quantity sales. Special discounts are available on quantity purchases by corporations, associations, and others. For details, contact the publisher at the address above.

Library of Congress Control Number: 2020910636
ISBN-13:   978-1-64620-379-6   [Paperback Edition]
                  978-1-64620-380-2   [Digital Edition]

Rev. date: 07/24/2020

CHAPTERS

PREFACE

This workbook is designed to uncover the ugly truths that we as women hide and cover daily. It will provide you the opportunity to reflect on your life from your earliest memories and how those play a role in *who* you are today. This road map is to provide you with a sense of self. I hope that you revisit this workbook several times throughout the years to understand how you evolve and to show that you are in a constant improvement stage. This journey will help you unpack memories and experiences that stand in your way of living your best absolute life. This manual is not intended for you to go through in one day or even one week. You want to pace yourself and ensure that you are free of distractions so that you can be in tune with your feelings and heart when completing this workbook.

As working women and women on the go, I understand that setting aside time to dedicate in properly applying yourself to self-help and personal growth methods may be a little daunting and, let's face it, time-consuming. However, it is imperative to fill our bucket and understand that if we as women are functioning below 100 percent, we can't possibly be the best mother, daughter, friend, girlfriend, wife, or anything else you can think of. Being self-aware is probably the most important thing you can do for yourself.

The goal is to have you carve out fifteen to twenty minutes per day so that you can fully self-assess and analyze your potential growth and development. For me, the best time was at the end of my workday, after I had come home from teaching, preparing dinner, helping my children with their homework, spending quality time, bathing them, and putting them in bed at 8:30 p.m. —faithfully! At that time, I then began to wind down. To be honest, it's the absolute best for me as I love spending time with myself!

My end goal for you after completing this workbook is for you to not necessarily have all your issues and insecurities sorted out; however, if I can help you shed some light on some of your behaviors and thought patterns and lead you to dig deeper, I've done my job. For a lot of women, they haven't been exposed to this type of approach of meaningful and necessary self-assessment. I want you to know that it was destined for you to read and experience this workbook.

You know you are ready for this workbook when you are simply *tired of yourself.*

As a disclaimer, I am not a medical doctor, so the various exercises that you are about to participate in are ones that have helped me come to a greater understanding of myself. I am simply a woman who has gone through some experiences and came to the realization that I needed some help with my mental thinking.

I also want to leave you with this: given your history and upbringing, you have the power either to be or remain the victim or become the Victor! You have the power to break chains, old habits, and family curses.

This personal road map belongs to

_____

aka Queen

The best project you'll ever work on is you.

ACKNOWLEDGMENT

First and foremost, I'd like to take this time to thank my Lord and Savior Jesus Christ, without whom there would be no Ms. Juli Marie. I want to thank my two amazing daughters, Marianah and Qalese, for allowing me to be their compass. I want to thank my parents, John and Betty, for always pushing me to my full potential. I would also like to thank Jessica, Remi, LaShonnda, Ramycia, and Earshline for challenging me and for helping me to zone in on my soul and figure out myself!

I want to also thank my cousin Deon for being a listening ear during my life's trials, tribulations, and providing me a good laugh when I wasn't thinking so clearly.

CHAPTER 1

LABEL ME

For this first exercise, I would like you to use the space below. Put your name in the center circle, and using the web bubbles write in at least ten to fifteen words that describe who you are as a person (good and bad). Be honest! Feel free to draw more bubbles if needed. Be sure to include words or phrases that people have called you as well.

The purpose of this exercise is to view yourself and to list the description of yourself so that you can evaluate them. Are your words positive, negative, or a mixture of both? You want to ensure that when you are thinking of yourself, you need the truth.

When complete, I want you to put an *X* through some words that are negative and are not growth words and repeat to yourself, "I will not allow these words to be me."

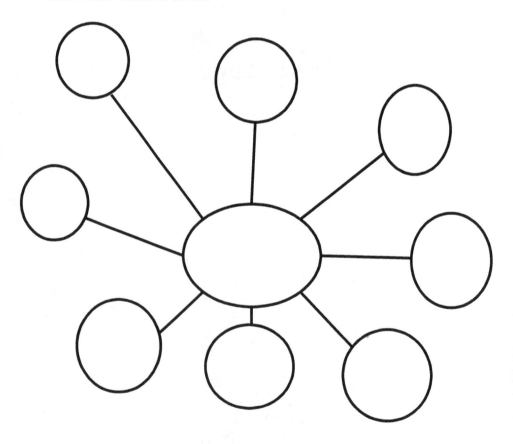

Reflection Space

After each section of this workbook, I've included some space for you to write down your thoughts and reflections pertaining to the exercise. In order to grow and recognize yourself, it's best to write down your initial thoughts.

_____

_____

_____

_____

_____

_____

_____

_____

_____

_____

_____

_____

_____

_____

CHAPTER 2

MEMORY LANE

Childhood Memories

This activity is intended for you to reflect on your upbringing. A lot of women are affected at this stage of their life, and it would help if you took the time to sit and think deeply about these things.

For this next exercise, I would like you to write a little about your history, including fun, exciting pivotal moments. Take a moment and think about your childhood. Who did you live with? How was your overall childhood experience? Did anything happen to you that you haven't told anyone? Who was your best friend at the time? What preschool and elementary school did you attend? Who was your favorite teacher? Why? What fun things do you remember growing up? Did you enjoy the outdoors? Were you raised by a single parent or both? Or were you in foster care? How did that make you feel?

_____

_____

_____

_____

_____

_____

_____

_____

_____

_____

_____

JULI MARIE M.ED

Middle School Memories

Similar to the questions that you answered and wrote about in your childhood, I want you to think a little deeper about your middle school experience. Think about your homelife, parents, and siblings. Were you a loner or the life of the party? Were you a quiet girl or the boisterous? Were you allowed to date? Were you "boy crazy"? Did your parents tell you about boys and dating? Did you focus on your friendships? Did you have that person that you shared your deepest secrets with, or did you have a diary? Did anything happen traumatic to you? Did you participate in any after-school clubs? What school did you attend? Recall a time when you felt hurt by a classmate, friend, or teacher. Were you suspended at all, and why?

_____

_____

_____

_____

_____

_____

_____

_____

_____

_____

_____

JULI MARIE M.ED

High School Memories

How were you in high school? What type of friends did you hang around? Were you a studious student? Were you allowed to date? Talk about your parents, friends, boyfriends/girlfriends. How did you view yourself in high school? Describe your thoughts about the young woman that you were at this stage. If you could give your high school self some advice, what would you say to her and why? Were you an attention seeker? Did you lash out by sneaking out the house or doing other things? Did you have a job? Where?

_____

_____

_____

_____

_____

_____

_____

_____

_____

_____

_____

_____

_____

JULI MARIE M.ED

Post-High School/Adult Memories

This section is dedicated to the time when you graduated from high school and whatever you did after high school. Think and write down any regrets, celebrations, births, marriages, changes in your relationships, and the friends and associations that you still have to this day.

_____

_____

_____

_____

_____

_____

_____

_____

_____

_____

_____

_____

_____

_____

JULI MARIE M.ED

CHAPTER 3

IDENTIFYING CURRENT AND PAST HURTS AND HOW YOU DEALT WITH THEM

For this exercise, I would like you to list each hurt or traumatizing event that you've experienced and identify *how* it affected you and what have you done about it? Does it affect your everyday life, or have you pushed it into the back of your mind (e.g., failed marriage/relationship, infidelity, career opportunity, abuse [sexual, physical, mental, emotional], natural disaster, etc.).

Taking your power back and having the accountability to heal from your hurt will make a whole world of a difference if you put your all into this activity. Will it be pretty? It shouldn't be! You will come to the hard conclusion that you may be limiting not only yourself, but your potential by holding on to past hurts.

Unhealed childhood trauma can manifest as follows:

- Fixing others aka having a healing spirit
- People pleasing
- Codependency
- External validation needed
- Living on high alert
- Tolerating abusive behavior
- Attracting narcissistic partners
- Difficulty setting boundaries
- Fear of abandonment
- Perfectionism

If you are not ready for this specific activity, I would encourage you to skip it and return to it when you are ready. Your mind has to be ready to be honest and forgive, and your heart has to be ready to be truthful and stretched. A lot of women, including myself, are very hesitant to be vulnerable. It means that we have to strip and take down the walls that we put up. Doing this activity alone allows you to speak to your inner self. You have to understand when things happen to you good or bad, they didn't happen TO you, those things and situations happened FOR you!

Hurt 1	Hurt 2	Hurt 3
How did it affect you?	How did it affect you?	How did it affect you?
What have you done or what do you intend to do about it?	What have you done or what do you intend to do about it?	What have you done or what do you intend to do about it?

Hurt 4	Hurt 5	Hurt 6
How did it affect you?	How did it affect you?	How did it affect you?
What have you done or what do you intend to do about it?	What have you done or what do you intend to do about it?	What have you done or what do you intend to do about it?

Before going on to reflect, I'd like you to complete each of these statements that begin with "I survived..." and fill in with the hurts that you described on the previous pages.

I survived _____

I survived _____

I survived _____

I survived _____

I survived _____

I survived _____

Use the below space to reflect on your past hurts. Think deeply about what you want to do with all the cuts, bruises, and negative experiences. This step is critical in healing and in getting you to your destination of *peace*.

_____

_____

_____

_____

_____

_____

_____

_____

_____

_____

_____

_____

_____

_____

JULI MARIE M.ED

CHAPTER 4

MENTAL HEALTH ASSESSMENT

Since we are digging deep into your past, I think it's rather important that we also dig into your mental health. Your mind literally controls everything about you: your preferences, your dislikes, your demeanor, your decision-making, your achievements, your downfalls, how you perceive the world around you, and, most importantly, your thoughts about yourself. It's important to realize that our mind is the key to our success. We as women have to learn to rewire our brains continuously. Happiness is directly related to what is in our mind. When your mind is healthy and clear, we look at situations differently and without the unnecessary toxicity and cloudiness.

Living through a traumatic experience also plays a huge part in your mental health. You may find yourself replaying the incident(s), and you may also do things in your life to protect others from the potential of it happening again.

Take a moment and answer the questions below:

1. What does mental health mean to you?

2. Have you ever experienced a terrible occurrence that has impacted you significantly? Examples may include, but aren't necessarily limited to, being the victim of armed assault, witnessing a tragedy happen to someone else, surviving a sexual assault, or living through a natural disaster.

3. Do you ever feel that you've been affected by feelings of edginess, anxiety, or nervousness?

4. Have you experienced a week or longer of lower-than-usual interest in activities that you usually enjoy? Examples might include work, exercise, or hobbies.

If you struggle with answering these questions or are still are seeking closure with something, I would encourage you to reach out to someone you trust, maybe your religious leader, a parent, a friend, or a professional. Talk with this person and discuss strategies to help you unpack what's truly in the way of you having a healthy or healthier mindset. I want you to also understand that you are not the only one that may suffer from an unhealthy mental state. It took me months, and I'm still working out keeping a positive mind frame.

Some women may or may not consider if they've had a traumatic experience based on the fact that the situation was normalized by family members and/or friends. The three types of trauma include the following:

- Acute: where there was an incident that happened only once (bullying, sexual abuse, an accident, victim of a crime, or natural disaster)
- Chronic: where the incident was repeated or prolonged (domestic violence, sexual/physical/mental abuse, violence exposure, or neglect)
- Complex: where multiple incidents occurred and varied in severity over a span of time (moving, divorce, death of a friend/ family member, chronic illness, prison, new household member)

What we choose to call trauma is subjective. There are women that I've spoken to that have been sexually abused, and for some, it affects them severely and for others, I couldn't even tell. The important thing about trauma is understanding that just because an event or a series of events were "normalized" when we were younger doesn't make it normal or okay and it's up to you to recognize, take note, forgive, and overcome.

I would also recommend doing this daily: upon waking up, I make up my mind that today will be a great day! This goes into affirmations, which we will discuss later.

Reflection Think Ta nk

Below are multiple questions that are used as a great way to jump-start self-reflection (Woronko, N. D.). Revisit these anytime you're feeling unsure of yourself.

- Am I using my time wisely?
- Am I taking anything for granted? Am I employing a healthy perspective? Am I living true to myself?
- Am I waking up in the morning ready to take on the day? Am I thinking negative thoughts before I fall asleep?
- Am I putting enough effort into my relationships? Am I taking care of myself physically?
- Am I letting matters that are out of my control stress me out? Am I achieving the goals that I've set for myself?
- How am I feeling right now?
- Have I forgiven myself for my past? What am I afraid of?

CHAPTER 5

GRATITUDE

Gratitude is known to increase positive emotions and happiness. Writing down what you are grateful for can help you become happier, thus leading to a more fulfilling life.

Did you also know that being a blessing to someone can cause a boomerang effect that can lead to a better life for you as well? Whether it is volunteering your time at a shelter, food bank, or a secondhand clothing store. I know what you're thinking. *What is one hour a week going to do?* More than you know! You want a blessing, be a blessing! You have more than most, especially if you have the opportunity to read this book.

Take a brief moment and just jot down some things that you are grateful for.

CHAPTER 6

GOALS

Let's begin with the goals that you have accomplished so far this year. No matter how small they may seem to you, list them! Take pride and celebrate in your ability to follow through!

1. _____

2. _____

3. _____

4. _____

5. _____

(Extra Space if needed)

_____

_____

_____

_____

_____

_____

_____

_____

_____

_____

JULI MARIE M.ED

This section is devoted to writing some of your goals in the following related areas. When writing goals, you must make sure that they are SMART goals, meaning that they are specific, measurable, attainable, relevant, and time-based. I've spoken to so many women that don't set goals for themselves because they say they don't have the time nor the effort to follow through. I challenge you to write at least two to three goals for each area and write them again somewhere where you'll see them every day and make sure you work on them.

Personal - This is anything that strictly has to do with only you (e.g., spiritual/religious, building more knowledge, treating yourself once a month, spending quality time alone or with children, joining an organization, saving money, getting out of debt, etc.).

1. _____

2. _____

3. _____

Employment/Career Related

1. _____

2. _____

3. _____

Fitness/Health-Related

1. _____

2. _____

3. _____

Family-Centered - These goals have to deal with your family and/or close friends (e.g., mending broken relationships, forgiving a family member, better communication with family, dedicating more time to your family, etc.).

1. _____

2. _____

3. _____

CHAPTER 7

REFLECTION ON PARENTS

Use this T-chart, and label "Mom" and "Dad." If you had an absent parent, you may substitute it with whoever played an important role in your upbringing.

Think of something that you remember from each person. It could be a saying or a recipe. How did this person make you feel? Are you close with them? Have they passed on? What are your true feelings about this individual?

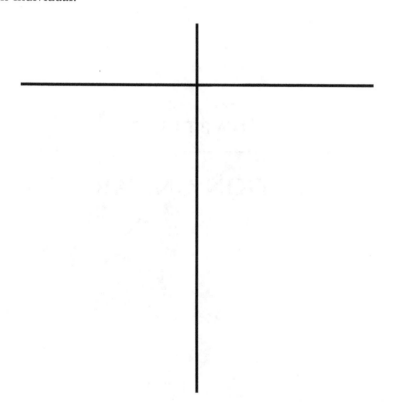

The purpose of this activity is to bring that nostalgia or the memory of a person that raised you and how you view them. Are you similar or different from them?

CHAPTER 8

HOW DO YOU SEE YOURSELF?

How you view and treat yourself is how others will view and treat you. If you call yourself a queen and promote nothing but positivity, peace, and calmness, then the people in your life will either rise to your standard and treat you as such or they will leave because they are unwilling or can't, which is okay. However, if you are always in a bad mood, downtrodden, negative, and don't think too highly of yourself, think why would anyone else treat you otherwise.

Multiple factors can affect your self-esteem. Your childhood, society, the media, and people in your life can all add or take away on how you feel about yourself. Studies have shown that people who have unhealthy self-esteem are more likely to experience stress, anxiety, and depression.

The goal of this chapter is to help you invoke some thoughts about yourself. Answer to yourself. Use your cell phone to record yourself so that you can later revisit your answers.

Why do I matter?	What are the things that make me self-aware?
Do I consider myself to be authentic? How and why?	Do I accept me for who I am? Am I comfortable with me?
Am I empathetic? In other words, am I sensitive to other people's needs?	How do I face adversity or fears?
Who do I surround myself with?	What positive things or habits can I do in my life to enrich it?

Why do I matter?	What are the things that make me self-aware?
Do I consider myself to be authentic? How and why?	Do I accept me for who I am? Am I comfortable with myself?
Am I empathetic? In other words, am I sensitive to other people's needs?	How do I face adversity or fears?
Who do I surround myself with?	What positive things or habits can I do in my life to enrich it?

Have I forgiven others who have lied, cheated, done me wrong?	What do I want to see in my life in the next five to ten years?
Describe a time where I thought my life was *over* however the situation turned out to be a blessing.	What are three things that I do exceptionally well but take for granted?
Currently, what is my confidence booster song?	Why is my life so good?
Who am I becoming?	What extraordinary people or experiences would I like to attract today?

What would I do if I had *no* limits?	How can I maintain a positive mindset?
Since I am in control of my life, what are some things I can do to enrich it?	How can I inspire others?
What inspires me?	What is my special gift?
What can I start doing to strengthen my emotional balance? What can I stop doing?	What is one small change I can make to this week that will help me feel in control of my life?
In terms of finances, what changes could I try to make to feel more confident financially?	How do I spend my downtime?

CHAPTER 9

POSITIVE SELF-TALK

For this exercise, I want you to start with five deep breaths.

Inhale...Exhale...
Inhale...Exhale...
Inhale...Exhale...
Inhale...Exhale...

I want you to think and list every single positive word that you can think of that describes you right now. Filling the hearts and open space with nothing but positivity should immediately give you a boost of confidence, self-love, self-admiration, and a greater sense of self. This exercise is also good if you have a preteen or teenage daughter(s).

CHAPTER 10

THE POWER OF MANIFESTATION

Creating manifestations is a helpful way to clear your mind and put things in perspective. Manifestations can be defined as positive phrases or statements used to visualize an abundant future for you.

Every December 31, I sit down with my children and we write down five to ten things that we'd like to see come to fruition in the next year, similar to a wish list. The most important thing about writing manifestations is *how* you write them. Instead of writing, "I will lose twenty pounds next year," choose to rewrite as if it already happened: "I *lost* twenty pounds next year." You notice that when you write your manifestations as though it already happened, it kind of tricks your mind into it already happening, thus telling the universe that whatever it is has already happened—if that makes sense.

I find that it's also important to write the date when you wrote the manifestation next to it so that when it happens, you'll be able to see how long it took for the manifestation to come to you.

Disclaimer: There have been manifestations that I wrote five years ago that I'm still waiting for them. I continue to rewrite it down and to have patience! The thing about manifestations is that we don't know *when* they're coming.

Examples: I met my husband, I graduated with my masters, I volunteered more at the local school, I was a better mother to my kids, I was a better daughter to my parents…you get the point.

This exercise is something that I do quite frequently. What do you want to see happen in your life? Picture it, walk in it, and have faith that it will come to pass!

Date Written:

Example: (5/1/19) I started my own catering business.

1. _____

2. _____

3. _____

4. _____

5. _____

6. _____

7. _____

8. _____

9. _____

10. _____

CHAPTER 11

FREEWRITE CHALLENGE

These next four to five days, I want you to freewrite whatever comes to your mind. Write about your life currently, how has thinking positively changed your outlook, what happened today, how has this road map helped you, would you consider sharing your thoughts with close girlfriends at a girl's night, etc.?

And *go!*

_____

_____

_____

_____

_____

_____

_____

_____

_____

_____

_____

_____

_____

JULI MARIE M.ED

JULI MARIE M.ED

JULI MARIE M.ED

CHAPTER 12

FINAL THOUGHTS FROM THE AUTHOR

Yass, girl! You made it! Congratulations on completing *your* journey. You should have a clear indication of who you are; why you are the way you are (good and bad); and learned some strategies to identify, recognize, and remove any toxic traits that you may have. We have to remember that some experiences that happened in our lives have shaped us into the women that we are today. Remove the anger from the past, remove the hurt from the past, remove any and everything that is standing in the way of your true destiny, and, most importantly, forgive yourself! You went through this workbook and probably didn't even realize that you were also strengthening your accountability. You were made aware of your past, you reflected, you made goals to better yourself, you reflected, you identified your hurts and successes, and again you reflected. Being able to reflect on experiences gives us power. We as women can stand and say, "No matter what, life happened and I *conquered*!"

I want to thank you for taking the time out to read and be a part of this workbook experience. I hope you found it to be useful and will continue to use it throughout your life. I pray that you—yes, *you*—host a gathering with some of your closest girlfriends and use this book as a talking piece. I hope that you share this workbook with a coworker, friend, and family member. There isn't a woman, young or mature, that this book couldn't help or shed some light on. I, again, thank you for your purchase.

Being that as it may, personally speaking, I've had quite some blows in my lifetime. I've gone through the abuse, the hurt, the shame, and the negligence of myself. Throughout the years my decisions and choices in men have led me on this road of recovery, strength, and power! As long as I know what I don't want in this life, it's very easy for me to decide what I do want and be able to picture it in my mind, tell God, and watch it happen. Or another way to think of it is, if something that I thought I wanted doesn't happen, all that is telling me is that I have something *better* coming. So I *win* either way!

There is an image below, and I want to further discuss what this picture means to me. There are three stages that a woman must pass in order to get to *self-worth*. The bottom or the largest piece of this picture is the foundation for the key points: self-awareness. In order to consider yourself a self-aware individual, you have to go through various activities such as this workbook and identify what makes you, you. You have begun this process, and it is my hope that you continue up the pyramid. Self-acceptance is learning to recognize faults and experiences and to forgive yourself. Can you honestly say to yourself that "I forgive myself" and mean it?

Once those two steps have been completed, you then graduate to self-love, which means that you are now making every decision based on your love for yourself! You are choosing not to engage in certain activity, you are choosing not to be used by an individual, you only communicate with people who truly have your best interest at heart, you only pour out positivity, you are constantly putting good karma out into the universe, and you will not indulge in *anything* that will put yourself in a negative headspace.

Once you've mastered those three steps, you have arrived at self-worth! This is the Don Dada of them all. At this stage, you are knowledgeable and aware of every situation that you've gone through, good, bad, and the ugly. You have accepted your failures and flaws and learned some tough lessons. You have become so attuned with yourself that you refuse to go back to dead relationships, lessons that you've overcome, failures, negative mindsets, feelings of less than, anxiety, depression, and overthinking.

The crazy thing about this visual is just because you arrive at the top of the pyramid does not guarantee that you stay there! You have to become so headstrong that no matter what is thrown your way, you have to stay atop of this pyramid like the true queen you are! Now, don't say I didn't warn you, but you *will* be tested—that's a guarantee. Old and dead situations and people will start to show up just to see if they can pull you back, but an old song comes to my mind, and it's called "I Can't Go for That" by Daryl Hall and John Oates.

I leave you with this final thought: you are destined for *greatness*! Chin up, girl. You are not who you were a year ago! Celebrate that and keep it movin', Queen!

Psst... Bonus Chapter

Affirmations

Affirmations are positive sayings that not only encourage yourself but if repeated and believed, you will start to accept and hold to be true that you are whatever you say you are! I have written ten affirmations that I have posted in both my bathroom and my daughter's bathroom; and every time that I am in there, whether it be washing my hands, brushing my teeth, cleaning, etc., I read it aloud.

Repeat these three times a day for the next ten days. What if someone told you that just repeating positive words to yourself often could change your mind and your life? Read when you wake up, set an alarm for lunch, and then again before you lie down for bed.

Circle at least five to eight affirmations that you would like to repeat to yourself for the next ten days.

I am smart.	*I am bold.*
I am powerful.	*I attract financial abundance.*
I am courageous.	*I am at peace.*
I am forgiving.	*I am worthy.*
I am humble.	*I am enough.*
I am favored.	*I am unstoppable.*
I am loved.	*I am beautiful.*
I am grateful.	*I radiate positivity.*
I am capable of loving.	*I am confident.*
I am gifted.	*I am healthy.*
I am creative.	*I am assertive.*

CPSIA information can be obtained
at www.ICGtesting.com
Printed in the USA
LVHW010348040920
665076LV00001B/150